Paul Woolery

2008

LIGHTNING SHOES

BY PAUL E WEATHINGTON

JuneKat Books
Atlanta, Georgia

ILLUSTRATED BY JONATHAN BASS

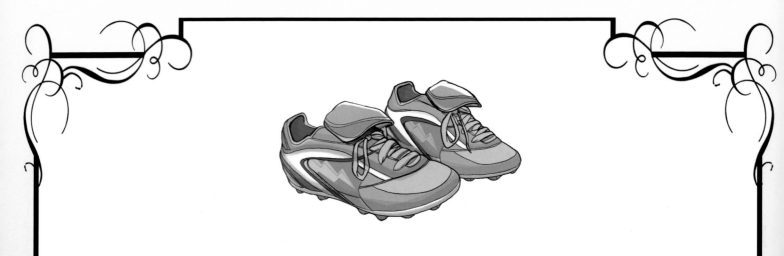

Published by
JuneKat Books, LLC
191 Peachtree Street NE, Suite 3900
Atlanta, Georgia 30303

ISBN 978-0-615-21807-6 (HC)
ISBN 978-0-615-24682-6 (SC)

10/07
E
Wea
SGL00144 $17.00

Library of Congress Control Number: 2008925759

Printed in Canada by Friesens Corporation

Jacket and book design by Burtch Hunter Design

Contact Information

For ordering information, upcoming books
and information on our company, please visit us on the web at:

www.JuneKatBooks.com

Or contact us by mail at:

JuneKat Books, LLC
191 Peachtree Street NE, Suite 3900
Atlanta, Georgia 30303
Telephone: 404-524-1600 • Fax: 404-524-1610

DeDicaTions:

To my two wonderful daughters, Shannon and Katherine, who have proven that the "Princess" title can be shared. Shannon, thanks for all the wonderful memories from the soccer field. I have been honored to be part of it.

To all of Shannon's soccer coaches and teams, including, "Pete's Dad," (John's Creek Methodist Intramurals) Greg Radloff (West Gwinnett), Dennis Ellenberger (Norcross Magic), Chris Nolen and Nathan Borror (Atlanta Fire United). To her High School soccer coaches at Woodward Academy, Tonia Webb and Louisa Boyle. To her trainers, Gene Patterson and Erin Marler who tried mightily to keep her patched up. A special tribute goes to Cathy Kupstas, Team Mom extraordinaire.

For Katherine and Paul Jr., and all the joy you are already producing on the soccer field. For Coaches Jody Tucker and Woody King for convincing Katherine she had "Lightning Shoes." For Charles Akin and Coach Jason Cree, Adam Tomlin and all the folks who make the Peachtree Road United Methodist Church Sports program a smashing success.

The book is dedicated to the Woodward Academy Varsity girl's soccer team (2006 Georgia State AAAA Champions) and Coach Tonia Webb and Coach Louisa Boyle and the Atlanta Fire United U-16 team 2006 Georgia State Cup Champions and Coach Chris Nolen.

Special thanks to Cy Strickler and The Tophat Soccer Club and to Woodward Academy for allowing the use of their images in the book.

Oh yes, and to soccer moms (and dads) everywhere. I pledge to comprehend the "off sides" rule before the final whistle sounds.

THANK YOU

She was a pretty little three-year-old girl who loved "girly things."

She played with dolls, makeup, jewelry— lots of pretty rings.

Her older brother was big and fast.
He played all sports and outdoor stuff.

She was very active with gymnastics and ballet. Her parents signed her up for soccer and said, "come on, all the little girls play."

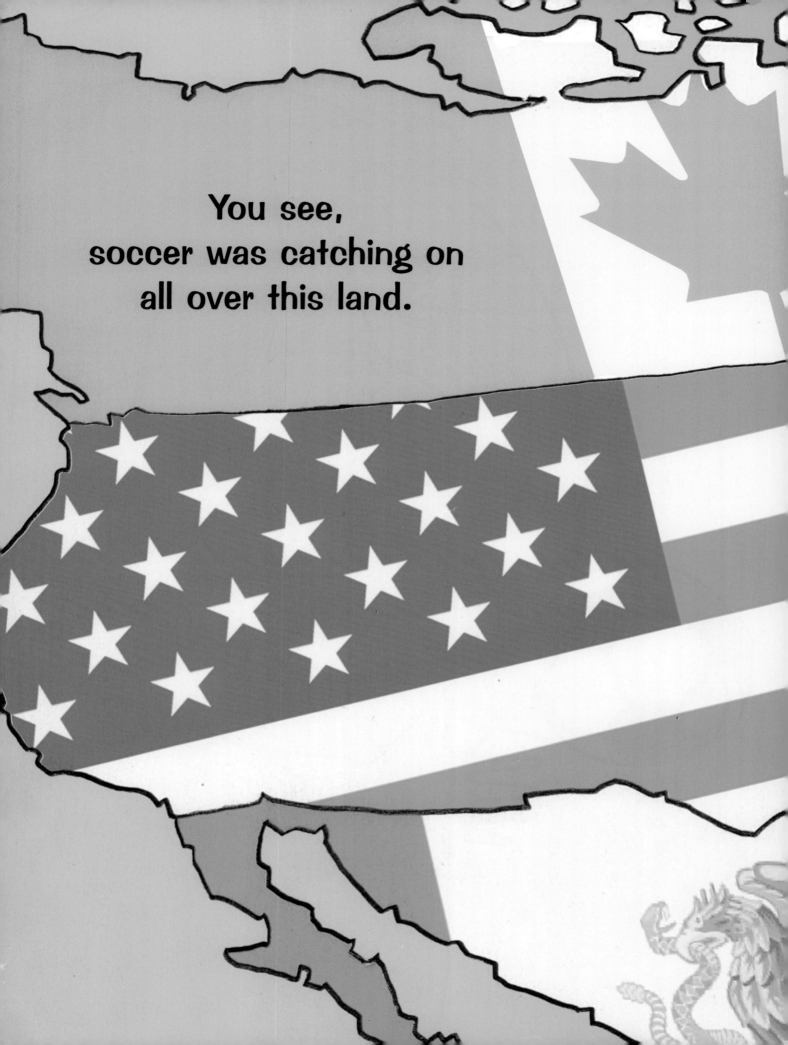

You see,
soccer was catching on
all over this land.

She was told to kick
the ball with her foot, but don't
touch it with her hand.

Her big sister
was already a soccer star,
earning a scholarship to college.

But the little princess
was just in preschool,
getting a head start on her knowledge.

So she joined the soccer team,
with her parents'
nudge and shove.

She ran on her tippy toes,
but she really wasn't fast.

She followed the other girls to the ball,
but many times was last.

Still, she was a
fashion statement
in her jersey
of Kelly green.

But some girls pushed
and shoved her,
she was just too sweet
to be that mean.

She liked going to the
games with her hair bows
and shoes of pink.

But after a few minutes
she'd leave the field
and sit down for a drink.

So it came time for the next season,
this time she was four.

She said she really wanted to play,
she'd even try to score.

She'd run as fast
as her little legs would go,
her cheeks flush bright red.

But she was more into
socializing than the score.
She never knew who was ahead.

Then one day it was like magic
when her coaches called her near.

"You have lightning in your shoes,"
they said to her, "run fast—
like you were a deer!"

When they saw how fast it made her,
the coaches were amazed.

They came up with a cheer
and this is how it was phrased:

"Lightning Shoes, Lightning Shoes,
run fast to the ball!!

Lightning Shoes, Lightning Shoes,
it won't hurt if you fall!!

Lightning Shoes, Lightning Shoes,
be fast, strong and bold!!

Lightning Shoes, Lightning Shoes,
score all your goals!!"

There was something about those words
that changed our little girl that day.

Now that she had "Lightning Shoes"
she was the fastest and made every play.

Instead, she scored lots of goals
and never wanted to come out.

"Lightning Shoes," what a clever name
to give her pink cleats.

We marveled at how a simple slogan
could inspire athletic feats.

You see, there was nothing new
or magic about our daughter's
"Lightning Shoes."

But some nice, creative coaches
had inspired her with
kind words and verbal cues.

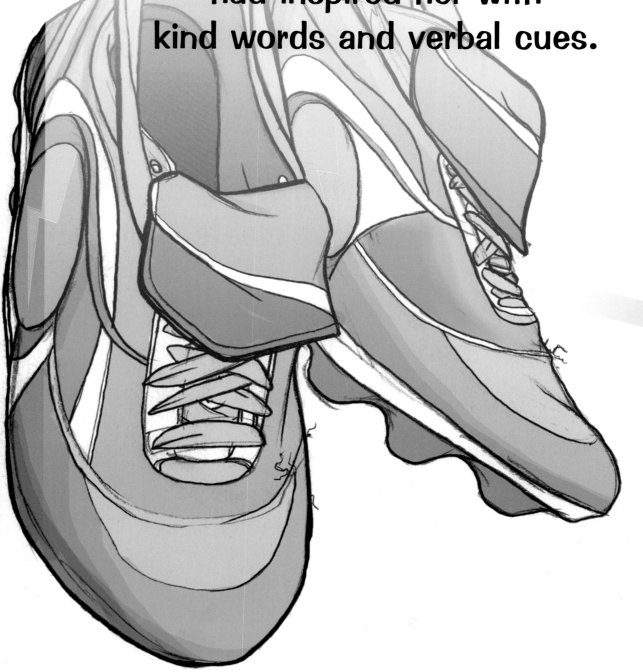

"Lightning Shoes, Lightning Shoes,
run fast to the ball!!

Lightning Shoes, Lightning Shoes,
it won't hurt if you fall!!

Lightning Shoes, Lightning Shoes,
be fast, strong and bold!!

Lightning Shoes, Lightning Shoes,
score all your goals!!"

From the soccer field to the classroom,
our little girl did go.
We watched her
mind develop.
We watched her
body grow.

But she always had her "Lightning Shoes" to help her with the books.

Her coaches' words stuck with her
throughout her school age years.

They helped her deal with laughter.
They helped her deal with tears.

Lightning Shoes, Lightning Shoes,
be fast, strong and bold!!

Lightning Shoes, Lightning Shoes,
score all your goals!!"

Soccer's simple teachings—
share the ball and stay onside,
seemed to make sense for the game of life.
Rules we parents should abide.

Now every time we face a new challenge
or tackle a new fear;

"Lightning Shoes, Lightning Shoes,
run fast to the ball!!

Lightning Shoes, Lightning Shoes,
it won't hurt if you fall!!

Lightning Shoes, Lightning Shoes,
be fast, strong and bold!!

Lightning Shoes, Lightning Shoes,
score all your goals!!"

Paul Weathington was born in Carrollton, Georgia. He is an Atlanta attorney who has written over 20 children's books. Mr. Weathington derives much of his material from his experiences with his seven children. He formed JuneKat Books, LLC in 2007. His other works may be seen and previewed at www.JuneKatBooks.com

Jonathan Bass was born in Chapel Hill, North Carolina. A graduate of the Savannah College of Art and Design in 2007, he currently works as a freelance artist and illustrator in Atlanta, Georgia.

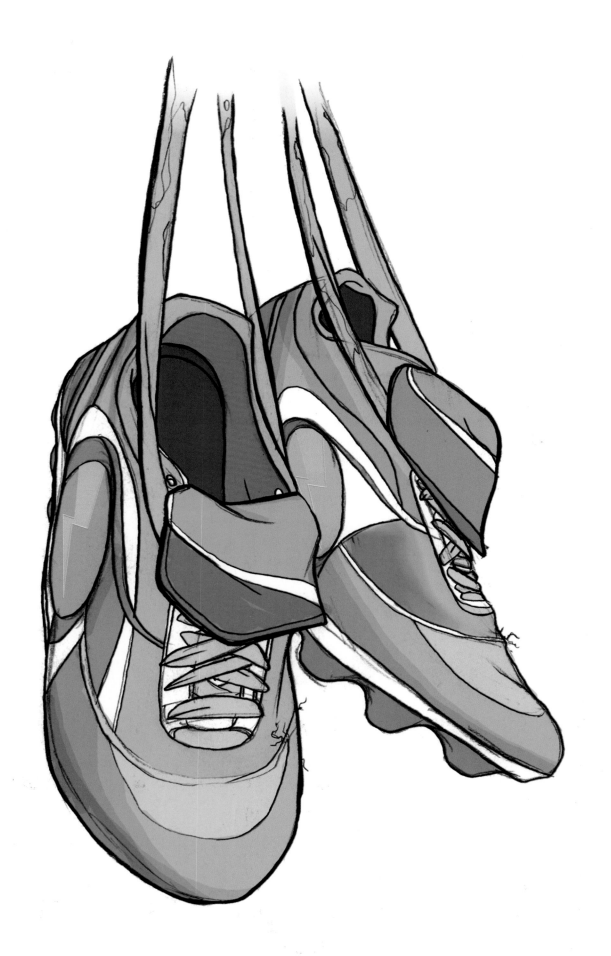

Other books by Paul Weathington

– Titles currently available –

Bed Bugs Don't Bite

Counting Sheep Doesn't Make Me Sleep

Where is the Man on the Moon?

Ish, Ish, Almost Made a Fish!

Lightning Shoes

– Upcoming releases –

Quick, Quick, I've Got a Cowlick!

The Amazing Adventures of Ned Neddington
(chapter books)